T

Buffalo Bills

OFFICIAL

All New

TRIVIA BOOK, II

Also by Scott Pitoniak

The Buffalo Bills Official Trivia Book

THE
Buffalo Bills
OFFICIAL
All New
TRIVIA BOOK II

Scott Pitoniak

ST. MARTIN'S PRESS
NEW YORK

Library of Congress Cataloging-in-Publication Data

Pitoniak, Scott.
    The Buffalo Bills official all-new trivia book II / Scott Pitoniak.
        p.   cm.
    ISBN 0-312-08151-0
    1. Buffalo Bills (Football team)—Miscellanea. I. Title.
GV956.B83P57   1992
796.332′64′0974797—dc20   92-20145
                                                                          CIP

First Edition: September 1992
10 9 8 7 6 5 4 3 2 1

To my special teams players—Susan, Amy, and Christopher.

CONTENTS

ACKNOWLEDGMENTS

The author would like to thank the following people for their contributions to the production of this book: Ed Abramoski, Scott Berchtold, Frank Bilovsky, Vic Carucci, Gary Fallesen, Larry Felser, Michael Galanti, Jamie Germano, Pete Knaus, Paul Kovacs, Annette Lein, Denny Lynch, Sal Maiorana, Charles McGillicuddy, Milt Northrop, Dave Owczarzak, Susan Pitoniak, Leo Roth, Bob Schranz, and George Witte. I'd also like to thank the following organizations: the Buffalo Bills, Gannett Rochester Newspapers, and the Pro Football Researchers Association of Western New York.

Jim Kelly doing something he prefers not to do too often—run with the ball. (Jamie Germano/Gannett Rochester Newspapers)

INTRODUCTION

Much has happened since we last pursued Bills trivia three years ago. Nomadic coach Lou Saban has added three more jobs to his already cluttered résumé. The Juice has made another movie. Freddie Smerlas, the most popular Bill of the 1980s, has left town and is now—say it ain't so, Fred—wearing enemy colors.

And the Bills have gotten better. Much better. In fact, the franchise has never enjoyed a more glorious stretch than this.

Four straight divisional titles. Back-to-back Super Bowl appearances. Thirty wins in its last 38 games. If you're a Bills fan, it truly has been a time to "Shout!"

The only downer, of course, has been the two Super Bowl losses. But there are worse things. Just ask any Bills fan who endured those consecutive 2–14 seasons not that long ago.

As Buffalo prepares for its thirty-third season, we've put together an all-new trivia book with questions and breakouts that we hope will test your knowledge, jog your memory, and, perhaps, stir a little friendly debate.

There are catchy nicknames, a revealing statistic or two, an all-time team that's sure to ruffle some feathers, and much more.

So buckle up your chin strap, get into your stance, and prepare for kickoff. Another journey through Bills trivia is about to begin.

—Scott Pitoniak
March 14, 1992

When it comes to catching the football, no one in Bills history has done it better or more often than Andre Reed. (Jamie Germano/Gannett Rochester Newspapers)

PRE-GAME
WARM-UPS

PRE-GAME WARM-UPS—QUESTIONS

1 Name the NFL head coach who was a roommate of Jack Kemp's at Occidental College in the 1950s.

●

2 Bruce Smith established a club record for sacks in a season during the 1990 campaign. How many did he have?
   a) 17
   b) 18
   c) 19
   d) 20

●

3 True or false: Thurman Thomas has rushed for more yards at a comparable stage of his career than any running back in Bills history.

●

4 What position did Andre Reed play for Dieruff High School in Allentown, Pennsylvania?

●

5 Match the Bill with the USFL team for which he last played.

Jim Kelly	Michigan Panthers
Kent Hull	New Jersey Generals
Dwight Drane	Houston Gamblers
Scott Norwood	Los Angeles Express
Ray Bentley	Birmingham Stallions

●

6 True or false: When James Lofton missed the 1991 regular-season finale against Detroit, it marked the first time in his fourteen-year NFL career that he had sat out a game because of an injury.

●

7 What number did Jim Kelly wear at East Brady, Pennsylvania, High School?

●

8 With which team did Bill Polian and Marv Levy first work together?
   a) Buffalo
   b) Kansas City Chiefs
   c) Montreal Alouettes
   d) Chicago Blitz

●

2

9 Which Bills offensive lineman lists house cleaning as one of his hobbies?

●

10 Who received the only game ball following the Bills' 51–3 rout of the Los Angeles Raiders in the AFC championship game?

●

11 The Bills have won 56 of 81 games since this player joined them.
 a) Jim Kelly
 b) Bruce Smith
 c) Cornelius Bennett
 d) James Lofton

●

12 Who was the first World League of American Football player to appear in a regular-season game with the Bills?

●

13 What was Frank Reich's record as a starter entering the 1992 season?

●

14 How many AFC East titles have the Bills won?
 a) 4
 b) 5
 c) 6
 d) 7

●

15 Name the three Bills who have been named Most Valuable Player of the Pro Bowl.

●

16 Which Bills tight end was invited to the Atlanta Hawks' training camp for a tryout?
 a) Pete Metzelaars
 b) Ernie Warlick
 c) Butch Rolle
 d) Keith McKeller

●

17 Who said: "Our head coach told us at our first meeting, 'Whatever you do, be nice to the cafeteria ladies because you need them to stay alive.' So I was always nice to them and they took care of me. I had a lot of midnight snacks. They'd bake cakes and all sorts of great desserts for me"?

WHAT'S IN A NAME?

In the beginning they were the Bisons. But team owner Jim Breuil didn't care for the name. He wanted something more imaginative. So before the start of Buffalo's second season in the old All-American Football Conference in 1947, he held a name-the-team contest.

One of the contestants, a man named Jimmy Dyson, suggested "Bills" after Buffalo Bill Cody, the famous nineteenth-century frontiersman. Dyson reasoned that the name was appropriate because Breuil's Frontier Oil company was sponsoring the team, and Buffalo was exploring a sports frontier of sorts with its new football franchise. Breuil liked the suggestion; Dyson was presented with a check for $500 and the team was renamed.

The league ceased operations in 1950, and when it was announced nine years later that Buffalo would be joining the new American Football League, the Buffalo *Evening News* held another name-the-team contest. About a thousand ballots were returned and scores of names suggested. Among them: Bruisers, Bees, Marauders, Condors, Bombers, Brutes, Bucks, Eries, and Red Jackets. One person even proposed calling them the Buffalo Wils after Ralph Wilson, the Detroit businessman who was bringing pro ball back to western New York.

The majority, though, cast their ballots for the Buffalo Bills, and Wilson, not one to buck tradition, gladly went along with public sentiment.

"The old team was a proud team," Wilson said. "Its fans had been very loyal. I could not see any reason why we should change the name."

4

Ralph Wilson with the greatest Bill of them all—O.J. Simpson. (Buffalo Bills)

18 What famous football-coach-turned-commentator advised Bruce DeHaven that his best shot at landing a pro job would be as a special teams coach?

19 Who dropped the potential game-winning touchdown pass with 14 seconds remaining in the Bills' 34–30 playoff loss to the Cleveland Browns following the 1989 season?

20 Who holds the record for most yards gained in a season by a Bills fullback?
   a) Jim Braxton
   b) Larry Kinnebrew
   c) Cookie Gilchrist
   d) Wray Carlton

21 True or false: Scott Norwood did not miss a field goal during the 1991 post-season.

22 Thurman Thomas wears No. 34 in honor of his boyhood football idol. Who was Thomas's hero?

23 Which coach has the most wins in Bills history?

24 How many passes did Steve Tasker catch while playing for Northwestern University?

25 Do the Bills have a winning record in post-season play?

26 Who was the Bills' leading ground-gainer in Super Bowl XXVI?

27 From 1988–91, the Bills won 34 of 37 games at Rich Stadium. Name the three teams that beat them at home.

28 With which team did Marv Levy begin his NFL coaching career in 1969?

29 What nickname was given to the '91 Bills defense that showcased linebacker Cornelius Bennett?

30 Every Bills fan knows that Whitney Houston's stirring ren-

dition of the "Star Spangled Banner" set the stage for Super Bowl XXV, but what song was blaring over the Tampa Stadium loudspeakers immediately following the final gun?

•

31 What is the only team to have beaten the Bills in a game in which Thurman Thomas rushed for 100 yards?

•

32 True or false: 1991 marked the first time in Bruce Smith's career that he failed to lead the Bills in sacks.

•

33 How many seconds did it take for the Bills to score 20 points in a 29–28 come-from-behind victory against the Denver Broncos in a September 30, 1990, game?

•

34 What current Bill has expressed a desire to become a general manager when his playing days are through?

•

35 What Bills linebacker led the team in tackles in 1991?
   a) Shane Conlan
   b) Cornelius Bennett
   c) Darryl Talley
   d) Carlton Bailey

•

36 What was the color of the Bills' helmets during their inaugural season in 1960?

•

37 What former Bill does the illustrations for Ray Bentley's *Darby the Dinosaur* children's books?

•

38 True or false: Gale Gilbert has never played in a regular-season game for the Bills.

•

39 Which two Bills were teammates at Mississippi State in the early 1980s?

•

40 Which Bills' modeling work has appeared in Sears' *Big and Tall* catalog?

•

41 How many times has Andre Reed topped 1,000-yards receiving in a season?

•

42 Who recruited Jim Ritcher to play football at North Carolina State?

43 Butch Rolle had 15 career receptions heading into the 1992 season. How many were for touchdowns?
   a) 5
   b) 8
   c) 10
   d) 12

44 Name the three Bills who have appeared in the Pro Bowl a club-record five times.

45 What two teams have never played a regular-season game at Rich Stadium?

46 True or false: The Bills have a winning record in overtime games.

47 Name the Bills running back who caught six passes for 127 yards in the Bills' 31–7 loss to the Kansas City Chiefs in the 1966 AFL title game.

48 Which linebacker made two interceptions in the Bills' 51–3 demolition of the Raiders in the 1990 AFC championship game?

49 This future Hall of Fame coach had lost ten of his last eleven games against the Bills entering the '92 season.

50 Where was Jim Kelly born?

Robb Riddick was always willing to go airborne to pick up a first down.
(Jamie Germano/Gannett Rochester Newspapers)

1. New Orleans Saints Coach Jim Mora.
2. (c) 19
3. True. After four seasons Thomas has gained 4,829 yards, compared to 4,046 for Joe Cribbs and 3,178 for O.J. Simpson.
4. Quarterback.
5. Kelly played with the Houston Gamblers, Hull with the New Jersey Generals, Drane with the L.A. Express, Norwood with the Birmingham Stallions, and Bentley with the Michigan Panthers.
6. True.
7. 11
8. (c) Montreal Alouettes. Levy was the head coach at the time and he hired Polian to do some scouting for him.
9. Mitch Frerotte.
10. Ralph Wilson.
11. (c) Cornelius Bennett
12. Punter Chris Mohr.
13. Reich was 4–2.
14. (b) 5. The years: 1980, '88, '89, '90, '91. The Bills also won the AFL's Eastern Division title three times, 1964–66.
15. O.J. Simpson, Bruce Smith, and Jim Kelly.
16. (d) McKeller declined the Hawks' invitation and also turned down an offer to sign a contract with the Wisconsin franchise in the Continental Basketball Association.
17. Howard "House" Ballard, who tips the scales somewhere around 340 pounds.
18. John Madden.
19. Ronnie Harmon.
20. (c) Cookie Gilchrist led the Bills and the AFL with 1,096 yards in 1962.
21. True. Norwood was a perfect five-for-five.
22. Former Houston Oilers' great Earl Campbell.
23. Lou Saban with 70, but Marv Levy was just nine behind entering the '92 season.
24. One.
25. No. They enter '92 with an 8–9 record in post-season.
26. Kenneth Davis with 17 yards on four carries.
27. Denver and New Orleans in 1989 and Detroit in '91.
28. Philadelphia Eagles.

29. The Sic 'em Defense.
30. Frank Sinatra's "New York, New York."
31. The New York Giants in Super Bowl XXV. Entering the '92 season, Buffalo was 24–1 in games when Thomas reached the century mark.
32. True. Injuries sidelined Smith for eleven of the Bills' sixteen games as he recorded a career-low 1.5 sacks.
33. 77 seconds.
34. James Lofton.
35. (a) Shane Conlan
36. Silver with blue numerals.
37. Mike Hamby.
38. False. Gilbert played in the second half of the Bills' 1990 season finale against Washington.
39. Center Kent Hull and cornerback Kirby Jackson.
40. Long-snapper Adam Lingner's.
41. Twice. 1989 and 1991.
42. Lou Holtz.
43. (c) 10.
44. Joe DeLamielleure, O.J. Simpson, and Fred Smerlas.
45. Seattle Seahawks and Tampa Bay Bucs.
46. True. Buffalo took an 8–3 overtime won–loss record into the '92 season.
47. Bobby Burnett.
48. Darryl Talley.
49. Don Shula.
50. Pittsburgh, Pennsylvania.

FIRST
QUARTER

1   The mother of this Bill played linebacker for the Los Angeles Dandelions in the Women's Professional Football League.
   a)   Carlton Bailey
   b)   Cornelius Bennett
   c)   Marvcus Patton
   d)   Ray Bentley

•

2   What former Bills receiver turned scout recommended that the Bills draft Andre Reed out of Kutztown State in 1985?

•

3   Match the Bill with his alma mater.

   Will Wolford   North Dakota State
   Chris Mohr   North Carolina
   Phil Hansen   Vanderbilt
   Carlton Bailey   Fresno State
   James Williams   Alabama

•

4   Name the three former Bills players currently employed as NFL head coaches.

•

5   True or false: James Lofton is the first player to catch a touchdown pass in the 1970s, '80s, and '90s.

•

6   Who led the Bills in tackles in Super Bowl XXV?
   a)   Jeff Wright
   b)   Cornelius Bennett
   c)   Leonard Smith
   d)   Darryl Talley

•

7   Name the three teams Joe Ferguson played with after being traded by the Bills before the 1985 season.

•

8   Which Bills running back has driven tractor-trailer trucks in the off-season and aspires to become a professional billiards player when his football days are through?
   a)   Jamie Mueller
   b)   Eddie Fuller
   c)   Carwell Gardner
   d)   Kenneth Davis

9 In the Bills' 1990–91 championship rout of the Raiders, Kelly set an AFC title game accuracy record by completing 79.3 percent of his passes. Which former Raiders quarterback held the record before Kelly?
a) Ken Stabler
b) Daryle Lamonica
c) George Blanda
d) Jim Plunkett

10 True or false: Scott Norwood has been more accurate kicking field goals in the post-season than the regular season.

11 In how many consecutive post-season games did Thurman Thomas rush for at least 100 yards, and what team snapped his streak?

12 Who has the highest yards-per-catch average among Bills receivers with at least 25 receptions?
a) Frank Lewis
b) Elbert Dubenion
c) Jerry Butler
d) James Lofton

13 What former Bills head coach is head coach of the Sacramento Surge of the World League of American Football?

14 Which Bill has been pictured on the front of a Wheaties box?

15 Who scored the points for the Bills in their 20–19 loss to the Giants in Super Bowl XXV?

16 The Bills' loss to the Redskins in Super Bowl XXVI extended the AFC's losing streak to how many games?
a) 6
b) 7
c) 8
d) 9

17 What position did Bill Polian play for the NYU football team?

CHRIS BERMAN'S
KIND OF TEAM

The ESPN announcer has never met a nickname he didn't like, which helps explain why Berman has adopted the Bills as his team. Buffalo has produced its share of catchy nicknames through the years. Here's a look at some of the more memorable ones:

NICKNAME	REAL NAME
Golden Wheels	Elbert Dubenion
Juice	O.J. Simpson
Pit Bull	Mitch Frerotte
The House	Howard Ballard
Biscuit	Cornelius Bennett
The Rockpile	Old War Memorial Stadium
The Electric Company	The offensive line that turned the Juice loose. It included guards Reggie McKenzie and Joe DeLamielleure, centers Bruce Jarvis and Mike Montler, tackles Donnie Green and Dave Foley, and tight end Paul Seymour
The Bermuda Triangle	Fred Smerlas, Jim Haslett, and Shane Nelson
Machine Gun Kelly	Jim Kelly
Hammerhead, Jughead	Shane Conlan
The Texas Twister	Kenneth Davis
The Mad Bomber	Daryle Lamonica
Squatty Body, Thurmanator	Thurman Thomas
Absorba the Greek	Fred Smerlas
Dr. Sack	Leon Seals

The Baby-faced Assassin	Harry Jacobs
Bootin' Tuten	Rick Tuten
Thunder Thighs	Ira Albright
The Sultan of Sayonara	Lou Saban
Tinker Bell	Greg Bell
The Dancing Bear	Ron McDole
Chill Factor 14	Frank Reich
Cookie	Carlton "Cookie" Gilchrist
Wild Angel	Steve Tasker
Joe D	Joe DeLamielleure and Joe Devlin
Bubby	Jim Braxton
Palace of Points	Rich Stadium
Mr. Peepers	Mark Kelso
Wiley	James Lofton
The General	Marvcus Patton
The Harley Boys	Mitch Frerotte and Glenn Parker
Earthquake Enyart	Bill Enyart
Marlin the Magician	Marlin Briscoe
Brew	Larry Kinnebrew
Darby	Ray Bentley
Ground Chuck	Name given to Chuck Knox's run-oriented offense
Fergy	Joe Ferguson
Wazoo	Dudley Meredith
Big Hoss	Ernie Warlick
Crawfish	Paul Guidry
Killer	Keith McKeller
The Blizzard Defense	Name given to the Bills defense in 1988
Abe	Ed Abramoski

Shane Conlan, shown here pressuring Colts quarterback Tom Ramsey, has had several nicknames, including Jughead, Hammerhead and Conlan the Barbarian. (Jamie Germano/Gannett Rochester Newspapers)

18 Name the two Bills who won Outland Trophies in college?

19 How many years had the Bills led the NFL in attendance heading into the '92 season?

20 Who blocked the field goal setting up Cornelius Bennett's 80-yard touchdown return in the Bills' stirring 29–28 come-from-behind victory against Denver in 1990?
   a) Nate Odomes
   b) Steve Tasker
   c) Robb Riddick
   d) Leonard Smith

21 True or false: The Bills established a team record for most points in the first quarter when they scored 24 in a 30–23 victory against the Philadelphia Eagles in a December 2, 1990, game.

22 Who was credited with snapping Dan Marino's streak of 759 pass attempts without being sacked?

23 What sportswriter was credited with coming up with the Bermuda Triangle nickname?
   a) Larry Felser
   b) Mike Dodd
   c) Gary Fallesen
   d) Vic Carucci

24 What's Howard Ballard's shoe size?

25 Who is second to O.J. Simpson in most rushing-receiving yards by a Bill?
   a) Thurman Thomas
   b) Andre Reed
   c) Joe Cribbs
   d) Cookie Gilchrist

26 His 91-yard kickoff return against the Raiders on December 8, 1991, was the first by a Bill for a touchdown since 1978.

27 True or false: Jim Kelly has never thrown for 400 yards in a regular-season game.

28   This Bill did not play organized sports until college.

29   Name the two Bills receivers who caught touchdown passes in Super Bowl XXVI.

30   Who scored the first regular-season points for the Bills in their inaugural game on September 11, 1960?

31   Which player has scored the second most touchdowns in Bills history?
   a)   Andre Reed
   b)   Thurman Thomas
   c)   Joe Cribbs
   d)   Cookie Gilchrist

32   How many field goals did Scott Norwood make during his record-setting 1988 season?

33   Whose record did Don Beebe tie when he caught four touchdown passes in a 1991 victory against the Pittsburgh Steelers?

34   How much money did Ralph Wilson pay for the Bills franchise in 1960?

35   Butch Byrd is the Bills all-time interception leader with 40. Who is second?

36   Did Ted Marchibroda have a winning record against the Bills when he coached the Baltimore Colts from 1975–79?

37   In the AFC championship game, who deflected John Elway's pass that Carlton Bailey intercepted and returned 11 yards for the only Bills touchdown in a 10–7 win?

38   Match the player with his number.

Fred Smerlas	34
Butch Rolle	70
Howard Ballard	75
Joe Devlin	76
Cookie Gilchrist	87

A BILL OF GOODS

At the press conference announcing his promotion to general manager of the Bills on December 30, 1985, he introduced himself as Bill Who? It worked because, at the time, the only household in which Bill Polian was a household name was his own.

My, how things have changed. These days, the feisty Irishman is known throughout Buffalo and the sporting world as one of the most astute judges of football personnel. Since he became GM, Polian's Bills have won four straight AFC East titles and have made two trips to the Super Bowl. Not bad, considering the Counterfeit Bills of '84 and '85 won just 4 of 32 games.

How did Buffalo Bill do it? Let us count the ways.

1. He hired Marv Levy to replace Hank Bullough midway through the 1986 season. Some accused Polian of cronyism because he had worked for Levy in Montreal, Kansas City, and Chicago. But if Polian was indeed doing a friend a favor, Levy has paid him back many times over, guiding the Bills to 61 victories in 95 games.

2. He signed Jim Kelly and several other USFL players who have contributed significantly to Buffalo's stampede. Kelly, of course, was the most important piece of the puzzle because the Bills hadn't had a legitimate quarterback since Joe Ferguson in the early 1980s. But Polian also signed Pro Bowl center Kent Hull, kicker Scott Norwood, linebacker Ray Bentley, and reserve defensive back Dwight Drane after the USFL went the way of the dinosaur.

3. He made The Trade. On Halloween Day, 1987, Polian sent two No. 1 draft picks, a No. 2, and 1,000-yard rusher Greg Bell to Indianapolis in exchange for Cornelius Bennett, who has blossomed into a perennial Pro Bowler. The move enabled Shane Conlan to move to his natural position (inside linebacker) and took some of the double-team pressure off Bruce Smith, making the sack-happy defensive end even more dangerous.

4. He oversaw some superb drafts. He had a role in the '85

crop, which yielded Smith, Andre Reed, and Frank Reich. Also, the '87 draft, which produced six starters—Shane Conlan, Nate Odomes, Jamie Mueller, Leon Seals, Keith McKeller, and Howard Ballard. And, of course, who can forget the 1988 draft, in which the Bills selected Thurman Thomas, Jeff Wright, and Carlton Bailey.

5. He exploited the free agent market, acquiring people like James Lofton, Kenneth Davis, John Davis, Mark Kelso, Kirby Jackson, and Gale Gilbert, as well as the USFL signees.

6. He revamped the front office, hiring people such as College Scouting Director John Butler and Marketing Director Jerry Foran, and giving greater responsibility to Pro Personnel Director Bob Ferguson.

Bill Polian dealt two No. 1s to land Cornelius Bennett. The Bills got the best of the deal. (Jamie Germano/Gannett Rochester Newspapers)

39 Who fumbled the ball the most times in Bills history?
a) O.J. Simpson
b) Dennis Shaw
c) Joe Ferguson
d) Joe Cribbs

40 True or false: No running back has ever gained 200 yards against the Bills.

41 Who led the Bills in sacks in 1991?

42 Name the Bills defensive back who had three interceptions during the 1991 post-season.
a) Nate Odomes
b) Clifford Hicks
c) Mark Kelso
d) Kirby Jackson

43 Who is the only running back in pro football history besides O.J. Simpson to rush for more than 2,000 yards in a season?

44 Jim Kelly threw for five or more touchdowns twice during the 1991 season. Name the teams he victimized.

45 The '92 Bills had the opportunity to become the second team in NFL history to make three consecutive trips to the Super Bowl. What's the only team to accomplish this feat?
a) Minnesota Vikings
b) Miami Dolphins
c) Pittsburgh Steelers
d) Oakland/Los Angeles Raiders

46 What Bills safety went on to become the Washington Redskins' director of scouting?

47 Name the six Bills selected to the 1991 All-Madden Team.

48 Which of these Bills coaches began his stay in Buffalo with five consecutive losses?

 a) Lou Saban
 b) Hank Bullough
 c) Harvey Johnson
 d) Chuck Knox

49 In which season did Joe Cribbs return to the Bills from the USFL?

50 True or false: Jim Kelly rushed for more yards in Super Bowl XXVI than Thurman Thomas did.

FIRST QUARTER—ANSWERS

1. (c) Marvcus Patton's mom, Barbara, played for the Dandelions, making $25 a game.
2. Elbert Dubenion, the man who held most of the Bills' receiving records before Reed broke them.
3. Wolford attended Vanderbilt; Mohr, Alabama; Hansen, North Dakota State; Bailey, North Carolina; Williams, Fresno State.
4. Sam Wyche (Tampa Bay), Marty Schottenheimer (Kansas City), and Tom Flores (Seattle).
5. True.
6. (a) Jeff Wright with 11.
7. Detroit Lions, Tampa Bay Bucs, and Indianapolis Colts.
8. (d) Kenneth Davis
9. (d) Jim Plunkett hit 70.8 percent of his passes in the '83 championship game against Seattle.
10. False. Norwood has been slightly more accurate in the regular season (74.3 percent) than in the post-season (72.2).
11. Thurman gained 100 or more yards in four consecutive post-season games, the streak coming to an end in the 1991 AFC title game against Denver.
12. (d) Lofton with a 19.5-yards-per-catch average.
13. Kay Stephenson.
14. Jim Kelly.
15. Scott Norwood kicked a 23-yard field goal. Don Smith scored on a one-yard run. Bruce Smith fell on Jeff Hostetler for a safety and Thurman Thomas scored on a 31-yard run.
16. (c) 8.
17. Safety.
18. Jim Ritcher with North Carolina State and Bruce Smith with Virginia Tech.
19. Four.
20. (a) Nate Odomes.
21. False. On September 13, 1964, the Bills scored 31 in the first quarter against Kansas City.
22. Nose tackle Jeff Wright was the one who bagged Marino.
23. (b) Mike Dodd.
24. The House wears a size 16EE.
25. (a) Thurman Thomas.

26. Al Edwards.
27. True. Kelly's regular-season best was 392 yards in a 1991 game against the Cincinnati Bengals.
28. Offensive lineman Glenn Parker.
29. Pete Metzelaars caught a two-yard TD pass, while Don Beebe's scoring reception was from four yards.
30. Darrell Harper kicked a 35-yard field goal against the New York Titans at the Polo Grounds in the AFL opener for each team on September 11, 1960.
31. (a) Andre Reed has 50, just 20 behind club leader O.J. Simpson.
32. Norwood kicked 32 field goals, surpassing by four the previous record established by Pete Gogolak.
33. Jerry Butler's. Butler caught four touchdown passes in a 1979 game against the New York Jets.
34. Wilson paid a $25,000 franchise fee.
35. Tony Greene with 37.
36. Yes. Marchibroda's Colts won 6 of their 10 games against Buffalo.
37. Jeff Wright.
38. Smerlas 76; Rolle 87; Ballard 75; Devlin 70; Gilchrist 34.
39. (c) Joe Ferguson holds this dubious distinction with 76 fumbles.
40. True. The most yards ever gained against the Bills was 192 by the Jets' Freeman McNeil in a 1985 game.
41. Cornelius Bennett with nine.
42. (d) Kirby Jackson.
43. Eric Dickerson rushed for 2,105 yards with the Rams in 1984.
44. He had six against the Pittsburgh Steelers and five against the Cincinnati Bengals.
45. (b) Miami made it to the Super Bowl three straight years, 1972–74.
46. George Saimes.
47. Jim Kelly, Cornelius Bennett, Thurman Thomas, Will Wolford, Howard Ballard, and Steve Tasker.
48. (a) Lou Saban's 1962 team lost its first five games, but rallied to finish with a 7–6–1 record.
49. 1985. Cribbs spent one season with Buffalo before being traded to the San Francisco 49ers.
50. True. Kelly gained 16 yards on three scrambles, while Thomas was limited to 13 yards on 10 carries.

Ahmad Rashad before he became a television star. (Buffalo Bills)

SECOND
QUARTER

1 What Bill attended a baseball tryout at Three Rivers Stadium when he was 18 years old and was offered a contract by the Pittsburgh Pirates?

•

2 Have the Bills ever had two 1,000-yard rushers in the same season?

•

3 How many seconds remained on the clock when Scott Norwood's 47-yard field goal sailed wide right in Super Bowl XXV?

•

4 In 1991, Jim Kelly tossed 33 touchdown passes. Only four quarterbacks in NFL history have thrown more scoring strikes in a season. Name them.

•

5 Who was Kent Hull talking about when he said: "He's a lot like Art Shell was when he was a player—just a friendly bear quietly doing his job"?

•

6 True or false: Thurman Thomas out-gained MVP Ottis Anderson in Super Bowl XXV.

•

7 What player has the most interceptions against Jim Kelly?

•

8 What team did the Bills outbid to sign Richie Lucas, their No. 1 draft pick, in 1960?

•

9 What Bills running back was known as the Texas Twister in college?
   a) Thurman Thomas
   b) Greg Bell
   c) Kenneth Davis
   d) Keith Lincoln

•

10 Buster Ramsey was the first coach in Bills history, but he wasn't Ralph Wilson's first choice. To which Hall of Fame quarterback did Wilson originally offer the job?

11 Match the man with his hometown:

Marv Levy	Birmingham, Alabama
Cornelius Bennett	Cleveland
Ralph Wilson	Lebanon, Pennsylvania
Frank Reich	Detroit
Darryl Talley	Chicago

12 What Bill has been contacted by the WWF to pursue a career in professional wrestling once his football days are through?

13 This coach has the longest tenure of any assistant in Bills history.

14 In 1991 Thurman Thomas became the first player since (fill in the blank) to lead the league in yards from scrimmage three consecutive seasons.

15 Who did Bill Polian replace as Bills general manager?

16 True or false: Marv Levy's Kansas City Chief teams never qualified for the playoffs.

17 What former Bill played keyboard for a Buffalo-area band called Pulse?
   a) Cookie Gilchrist
   b) Spike Jones
   c) Butch Rolle
   d) Ray Bentley

18 Shane Conlan is tied for second in Penn State history for most tackles with this former Bills linebacker.

19 How many yards did James Lofton need to surpass all-time league leader Steve Largent entering the 1992 season?

20 Who forced a fumble on a punt return and also blocked a punt that J.D. Williams returned for a touchdown in the Bills' furious come-from-behind victory against the Raiders in a game during the 1990 season?

THE MISS

A few days before Super Bowl XXV, Scott Norwood was asked if he fantasized about winning football's premier game with a field goal in the final seconds.

Of course he had, the Bills kicker said.

"You start to think about what would be the ultimate for a kicker, and that would be it," he said.

"It could happen, and should that situation arise I won't have to hope or wish. I know that I'll be able to put it through."

That Sunday—January 27, 1991—the situation did arise, and Norwood's fantasy became his nightmare. The field goal attempt he had dreamed about, the difficult kick from 47 yards, sailed wide right with four seconds remaining, preserving the Giants' 20–19 victory in the most exciting Super Bowl of them all.

There may never be another Super Bowl like it for sheer emotion and drama. With the war raging in the Persian Gulf and an attack helicopter guarding the air space near Tampa Stadium, the Bills and Giants played a game for the ages.

Thurman Thomas was simply brilliant, rushing for 135 yards and catching five passes for 55 more. Despite the performance, Thomas was nosed out for most valuable player honors by Giants running back Ottis Anderson.

The Giants smash-ball approach won out over Buffalo's glitzy no-huddle as they held the ball for two-thirds of the game.

After the miss, Norwood walked dejectedly off the field, but he handled himself with remarkable grace in the post-game interviews, answering every question tossed his way.

The next day, about 30,000 fans gathered in Buffalo's Niagara Square to welcome back their heroes. They chanted, "We want Scott," until the teary-eyed kicker took the microphone and dedicated the ensuing season to them.

The Bills had lost, but what followed was clearly the triumph of the human spirit.

21 Who had the interception that ended the Bills' chances once and for all in their 34–30 playoff loss to the Cleveland Browns?

22 How many players were selected in the 1988 draft before Thurman Thomas?
  a) 29
  b) 39
  c) 49
  d) 59

23 Who holds the Bills record for most receptions in a season by a tight end?
  a) Pete Metzelaars
  b) Keith McKeller
  c) Ernie Warlick
  d) Mark Brammer

24 Carlton Bailey's 11-yard interception return for touchdown in the 1991–92 AFC title game against Denver marked the second time a Bills linebacker has turned a pick-off into a score during the post-season. Who was the other linebacker to accomplish the feat?

25 The Bills are one of three teams to lose consecutive Super Bowls. Name the others.

26 Who is the Bills' all-time receiving leader?
  a) Elbert Dubenion
  b) Bobby Chandler
  c) Jerry Butler
  d) Andre Reed

27 True or false: Kenneth Davis's 78-yard scoring run against the Indianapolis Colts was the longest run from scrimmage in the NFL during the 1991 season.

28 The Bills have a 7–15 record in the six domed stadiums they've visited. Name the only dome where they have an above-.500 record.

A picture's worth a thousand words, and this one says it all: Frank Reich and Scott Norwood walk numbly off the field after The Miss. (Annette Lein/Gannett Rochester Newspapers)

29 In a Monday night game against the Dolphins during the 1991 season, this Bill recorded a sack, forced a fumble, recovered a fumble, and returned it six yards for a touchdown—all on the same play.

●

30 In a 1962 game this quarterback threw six interceptions against the Bills.
   a) Tobin Rote
   b) George Blanda
   c) John Hadl
   d) Babe Parilli

●

31 True or false: Between 1988–91, the Bills had the best record in football.

●

32 Who pinned the most punts inside the 20 during their Bills career—Paul Maguire or John Kidd?

●

33 Who was Jim Kelly's favorite target during Super Bowl XXVI?

●

34 What team chose Ted Marchibroda in the first round of the 1953 NFL draft?
   a) Detroit Lions
   b) New York Giants
   c) Pittsburgh Steelers
   d) Chicago Bears

●

35 In how many games has long-snapper Adam Lingner started at center during his nine-year NFL career?

●

36 True or false: Andre Reed has led the Bills in receiving in each of his seven seasons with the team.

●

37 Who did Frank Reich back up at the University of Maryland?

●

38 What's Marv Levy's favorite baseball team?

●

39 What boxer has Bruce Smith been known to work out with?

SEE HOW THEY RUN

Here's a look at how O.J. Simpson, Thurman Thomas, and Joe Cribbs—the three most prolific rushers in Bills history—stack up in their first four seasons:

O.J. Simpson		Thurman Thomas		Joe Cribbs	
Year	Yards	Year	Yards	Year	Yards
1969	697	1988	881	1980	1,185
1970	488	1989	1,244	1981	1,097
1971	742	1990	1,297	1982	633
1972	1,251	1991	1,407	1983	1,131
Total	3,178	Total	4,829	Total	4,046

It should be noted that Thomas was the only one of the three not to be sidelined for any length of time during his first four seasons with the Bills. The Juice missed a total of seven games because of injuries in his first two seasons and also was hampered by a poor supporting cast (he joined a 1-12-1 team) and the misguided coaching philosophy of John Rauch, who thought Simpson would make a great decoy. Cribbs had his third season cut short by seven games because of the NFL players' strike. Both he and Thomas had another advantage over the Juice in that they began their NFL careers with contending teams.

40 Which kicker has had the longest tour of duty with the Bills?
   a) Scott Norwood
   b) Pete Gogolak
   c) John Leypoldt
   d) Joe Danelo

41 When did the Bills totally convert to the no-huddle?

42 Name the only receivers in Bills history to make at least 70 receptions in a season.

43 What Bill during the 1990 season became the first player to be named AFC defensive player of the week two weeks in a row?

44 What WLAF team did Chris Mohr play for?

45 Which Bill owns several car dealerships in Mississippi and Arkansas?

46 Who did Nate Odomes replace at cornerback during his rookie season in 1987?

47 Who was credited with a safety in Super Bowl XXV?

48 What former Bills quarterback was named MVP after guiding the London Monarchs to a 21–0 victory against the Barcelona Dragons in the 1991 WLAF title game at Wembley Stadium?
   a) Joe Duffek
   b) Willie Totten
   c) Bruce Mathison
   d) Stan Gelbaugh

49 Who accidentally bowled over Marv Levy while scrambling downfield on a punt during a 1991 game against the Colts?

50 What was Carlton Bailey's primary position at North Carolina?

Thurman Thomas has outgained the Juice and Joe Cribbs at a comparable stage of their careers. (Jamie Germano/Gannett Rochester Newspapers)

1. Shane Conlan. A standout catcher at Frewsburg, New York, High School, Conlan turned down a contract offer from the Pirates so he could play football at Penn State.
2. No. But they came close in 1975 when O.J. Simpson rushed for 1,817 yards and fullback Jim Braxton had 823.
3. Four seconds remained.
4. Dan Marino (48 TDs in 1984; 44 in '86); Y.A. Tittle (36 in '63); George Blanda (36 in '61); and Daryle Lamonica (34 in '69).
5. Howard Ballard.
6. True. Thomas rushed for 135 yards to Anderson's 102.
7. New England's Fred Marion.
8. The Washington Redskins, who had made the Penn State quarterback their top pick in the NFL draft.
9. (c) Kenneth Davis, who played his college ball at Texas Christian University.
10. Otto Graham, but he turned it down, saying he was content to remain as athletic director of the Coast Guard Academy.
11. Levy (Chicago); Bennett (Birmingham); Wilson (Detroit); Reich (Lebanon, Pennsylvania); Talley (Cleveland).
12. Mitch Frerotte.
13. Elijah Pitts. He begins his eleventh season with the team in 1992. Pitts was with the Bills from 1978–80, returned to the team in '85, and has been in Buffalo ever since.
14. Jim Brown.
15. Terry Bledsoe.
16. True, although his '81 Chiefs came within a field goal of beating out the San Diego Chargers for the AFC West title.
17. (c) Butch Rolle.
18. John Skorupan, who played with the Bills from 1973–77.
19. Lofton needed just 55 yards. He entered '92 with 12,987 yards on 699 receptions.
20. Steve Tasker.
21. Clay Matthews.
22. (b) 39
23. (a) Pete Metzelaars with 49 in 1986.
24. Darryl Talley returned an interception 27 yards for a score in the AFC championship game against the Raiders.
25. Minnesota and Denver.

26. (d) Andre Reed with 469 receptions.
27. True.
28. They are 1–0 at the Superdome.
29. Cornelius Bennett.
30. (b) George Blanda.
31. False. San Francisco was 48–16 during that span, one game better than the Bills.
32. Maguire. He had 130, while Kidd had 111.
33. James Lofton with seven receptions for 92 yards.
34. (c) Pittsburgh Steelers.
35. One. He was pressed into action during his rookie season with the Chiefs in 1983.
36. False. Greg Bell edged Reed out in 1985, but Reed has topped Buffalo's receiving list each year since.
37. Boomer Esiason.
38. The Chicago Cubs.
39. Pernell Whitaker in Virginia Beach, Virginia.
40. (a) Scott Norwood. The '91 season was his seventh with the team, one more than the previous longevity record set by Leypoldt.
41. Week twelve of the 1990 season against the Philadelphia Eagles.
42. Andre Reed (1988, '89, '90, '91) and Frank Lewis, who had 70 in 1981.
43. Cornelius Bennett.
44. Montreal Machine.
45. Kent Hull.
46. Charles Romes.
47. Bruce Smith.
48. (d) Stan Gelbaugh
49. Steve Tasker.
50. Nose tackle.

At 35, James Lofton shows no signs of slowing down. (Jamie Germano/ Gannett Rochester Newspapers)

HALFTIME

A TEAM FOR ALL-TIME

To paraphrase a former Bills coach who fought numerous losing battles with NFL opponents and the English language, we have a club that will take the sails out of your wind.

We have O.J. and a Cookie that won't crumble to carry the ball for our Bills All-Timers, and two sticky-fingered frequent fliers (Jerry Butler and Andre Reed) to catch it.

Up front we have earth-movers like Billy Shaw, Joe DeLamielleure, and Kent Hull. The President himself would be hard-pressed to find a more dependable group of bodyguards.

Speaking of high-ranking government officials, we have quarterback Jack Kemp, who went from yelling hut to working for HUD. But Jack doesn't start. That honor goes to Jim Kelly, the Machine Gun Kid from the cradle of quarterbacks, western Pennsylvania.

Our defense is like one of those blizzards that sweep in off Lake Erie and bury you. Listen to these names. Smith. Smerlas. Sestak. McDole. Conlan. Bennett. Stratton. I mean, who is going to run on these guys? They have more hits than Pete Rose, Elvis, and the Beatles combined. And if an opponent is foolish enough to test our secondary, Butch Byrd or Steve Freeman just might pick their pockets.

The special teams are just that—special. Forget The Miss. Scott Norwood virtually kicked the Bills to a 12–4 record in 1988. He split more uprights than anyone in club history and deserves the nod over Pete Gogolak and John Leypoldt. Our punter, Paul Maguire, can handle the swirling winds as easily as a microphone or a Budweiser. And don't think you are going coast-to-coast with one of his punts, because we have Steve Tasker racing downfield. He may look angelic, but he hits like the devil.

Our team will need a powerful personality to reign in all the egos. Lou Saban fits the Bills, but he rarely stays in town long enough for his mail to catch up with him, so we'll stick with Marv Levy, the only coach to lead Buffalo to the Super Bowl.

Since we like tradition (and real grass), we've decided to split our home schedule between old War Memorial Stadium and Rich. Sure, the Rockpile was kind of dumpy, but it had character, like those beer-and-a-shot-and-a-first-down Bills teams of the mid-1960s.

Here's a more detailed look at one man's All-Time Bills squad.

OFFENSE

Quarterback. Barring injury, Kelly will wind up as the club's all-time leader in every passing category. Kemp was very good and so was Joe Ferguson, but neither was as accurate as Kelly, who has guided Buffalo to four consecutive divisional titles and the franchise's only Super Bowl appearances.

Running back. No debate here. O.J. Simpson wins this race by several football fields. Of course, there won't be much of a drop-off when we go to our reserves, because Thurman Thomas and Joe Cribbs are talented enough to start for many all-time teams. Cookie Gilchrist is our selection at fullback. At six-foot-two, 243 pounds, he could scatter would-be tacklers as if they were bowling pins, and when he was willing to block, it was like having a pulling guard in your backfield. Plus, he can kick field goals and extra points if Norwood gets hurt. If Cookie does crumble, we can always call on two other brutes—Jim Braxton and Wray Carlton.

Wide receiver. We went with Andre Reed and Jerry Butler, but we wouldn't quibble if you decided to go with Bobby Chandler, Elbert Dubenion, Marlin Briscoe, J.D. Hill, James Lofton, or Frank Lewis. Reed runs precise patterns, has great hands, makes the catch in traffic, and has more moves than most running backs. Butler had world-class sprinter's speed and fabulous concentration. He would have been a Hall of Famer had he not wrecked his knee.

Tight end. Pete Metzelaars is a superb blocker and dependable receiver, but the starting assignment goes to Ernie Warlick. The Canadian Football League import averaged 17.2 yards per catch, one of the highest in club history. In time, Keith McKeller may play his way into our starting lineup.

Guards. Billy Shaw is a given. Because he played in the relative obscurity of the AFL and the Bills didn't make it to the Super Bowl, Shaw has never received serious consideration for the Hall of Fame. That's a shame because several defenders who played against him and are enshrined in Canton think Shaw belongs, too. The other guard spot goes to Joe DeLamielleure, who was voted into the Pro Bowl five times and teamed with Reggie McKenzie on the Bills' famed Electric Company line. It was difficult not to go with Jim Ritcher at one of the spots. But he, Reggie, and Tim Vogler give us solid backups.

Tackles. Joe Devlin and Stew Barber get the nod. When former New York Jets star Mark Gastineau was the league's premier pass-rusher, he always dreaded going against Devlin, who played more games in a Bills uniform than anyone. Barber, like Devlin, was a model of consistency for a decade.

Center. Kent Hull has gone to three Pro Bowls and is regarded by many GMs as the league's best at his position. Al Bemiller, who anchored the Bills' line during those AFL championship days of the mid-1960s, is our choice as backup.

DEFENSE

Ends. Bruce Smith and Ron McDole. Bruce is easily the greatest pass rusher in team history, the kind of player who, when healthy and happy, can dismantle an offense all by his lonesome. McDole was a 300-pounder with moves. The Bills made a humongous mistake in 1970 when they traded him to the Washington Redskins, where he turned in eight more productive seasons and was named to the Redskins' All-time team.

Tackles. Tom Sestak and Fred Smerlas. These two bouncers made a living bench-pressing blockers and ballcarriers. Sestak is another of the AFL Bills who deserve a bust in Canton. Smerlas, a five-time Pro Bowler, was a linebacker's best friend because he tied up blockers, clearing the way for the Hasletts, Nelsons, and Conlans to make the tackle.

Linebackers. This was the toughest unit to select. You could take the crew of Mike Stratton, Harry Jacobs, and John Tracey

Jim Kelly and Bruce Smith are major players on our All-Time Bills team.
(Jamie Germano/Gannett Rochester Newspapers)

from the 1960s or Cornelius Bennett, Shane Conlan, and Darryl Talley from this era and not go wrong. We decided to mix the old with the new, choosing Stratton, Conlan, and Bennett. Stratton is best remembered for delivering the hit heard 'round the world against San Diego Chargers running back Keith Lincoln in the 1964 championship game. But that was merely one of many brain-scrambling tackles he made during his ten-year Bills career. Conlan is a mud-and-blood 'backer who reminds some of former Steelers great Jack Lambert. The Bills gave up a lot to get Bennett in The Trade, but they haven't been disappointed. They've won four AFC East titles and made two Super Bowl appearances in his 4½ seasons in Buffalo. His presence enabled the Bills to move Conlan to his natural position (inside linebacker) and has taken some of the double-team blocking pressure off Bruce Smith.

Cornerbacks. Butch Byrd and Robert James. Byrd ranks as the team's all-time interception leader with 40, including 5 that he returned for touchdowns. James, out of tiny Fisk College, was discovered by Bills receiver-turned-scout Dubenion. James was a little guy who could fly and pack a wallop. Mario Clark, Charles Romes, and Tony Greene are our reserves.

Safeties. Steve Freeman and George Saimes. Freeman was neither fast nor big, but he was smart. Rarely was he caught out of position. Saimes was one of three Bills to be named to the All-time AFL team in 1969. Like Freeman, he was a thinking-man's football player, and boy could he hit. If Freeman or Saimes needs a blow, we can send in Mark Kelso or Bill Simpson.

SPECIAL TEAMS

Kicker. Norwood. There's a lot more to his legacy than The Miss as evidenced by his field goal accuracy of 74 percent, by far the best in Bills history. Should he falter, we can always call on Pete Gogolak, who revolutionized the game with his soccer style, or John Leypoldt.

Punter. Maguire over John Kidd and Billy Atkins. Maguire held the job for seven years and his 42.1 yards-per-punt average remains the highest in Bills history. Kidd was a superb coffin-corner kicker. He still holds the team record for most punts inside the 20, with 33 in 1985. Atkins was one of the more versatile players in Buffalo history. In 1961, for instance, he averaged 45 yards per punt and also intercepted ten passes.

Kick returners. Charley Warner and Wallace Francis. Warner returned three kickoffs for touchdowns during his career and averaged 25.6 yards per return. Francis averaged 27.2 yards per return and brought two kicks back for scores.

Punt returner. Keith Moody. The former Syracuse University star returned three punts for touchdowns in his four years with the team.

Coverman. Tasker. He's a kick coverer without equal and also occasionally blocks a kick or punt. Three times he has been selected to the Pro Bowl, solely on the basis of his special teams expertise.

Joe DeLamielleure (68) gets ready to clear a path for the Juice. (Buffalo Bills)

Fred Smerlas, one of our all-time defensive tackles, is about to get his huge arms on Doug Flutie. (Jamie Germano/Gannett Rochester Newspapers)

ALL-TIME ROSTER

OFFENSE

No.	Name	Pos.	Ht.	Wt.	Years with Bills
84	Ernie Warlick	TE	6–4	235	1962–65
83	Andre Reed	WR	6–0	190	1985–present
77	Stew Barber	T	6–2	253	1961–69
66	Billy Shaw	G	6–2	250	1961–69
67	Kent Hull	C	6–5	275	1986–present
68	Joe DeLamielleure	G	6–3	248	1973–79, '85
70	Joe Devlin	T	6–5	275	1976–82, '84–89
80	Jerry Butler	WR	6–0	178	1979–83, '85–86
12	Jim Kelly	QB	6–3	218	1986–present
32	O.J. Simpson	RB	6–2	205	1969–77
34	Cookie Gilchrist	FB	6–2	243	1962–64

DEFENSE

No.	Name	Pos.	Ht.	Wt.	Years with Bills
78	Bruce Smith	E	6–4	275	1985–present
76	Fred Smerlas	T	6–3	290	1979–89
70	Tom Sestak	T	6–4	270	1962–68
72	Ron McDole	E	6–4	289	1963–70
58	Mike Stratton	OLB	6–3	237	1962–72
58	Shane Conlan	MLB	6–3	230	1987–present
97	Cornelius Bennett	OLB	6–2	236	1987–present
20	Robert James	CB	6–1	184	1969–74
42	Butch Byrd	CB	6–0	211	1964–70
26	George Saimes	SS	5–10	195	1963–69
22	Steve Freeman	FS	5–11	185	1975–86

SPECIAL TEAMS

No.	Name	Pos.	Ht.	Wt.	Years with Bills
11	Scott Norwood	K	6–0	207	1985–1991
55	Paul Maguire	P	6–0	228	1964–70
89	Wallace Francis	KR	5–11	185	1973–74
22	Charley Warner	KR	6–0	176	1964–66
46	Keith Moody	PR	5–11	171	1976–79
89	Steve Tasker	KC	5–9	183	1986–present

THIRD
QUARTER

1   Name the two Bills to appear on the soap opera "General Hospital."

●

2   Who is the only running back in Bills history to have more than 100 yards rushing and 100 receiving in the same game?
   a)   Joe Cribbs
   b)   Thurman Thomas
   c)   O.J. Simpson
   d)   Cookie Gilchrist

●

3   True or false: Jim Kelly is the second most accurate passer in NFL history among quarterbacks who have attempted at least 1,500 passes.

●

4   Who is the Bills all-time leader in games played?
   a)   Fred Smerlas
   b)   Jim Ritcher
   c)   Joe Devlin
   d)   Steve Freeman

●

5   Who was the starting quarterback in the Bills' first game in 1960?

●

6   Who holds the Bills record for most points scored in a single game?
   a)   Cookie Gilchrist
   b)   Don Beebe
   c)   Jerry Butler
   d)   Scott Norwood

●

7   Name the two seasons in which the Bills went unbeaten at home.

●

8   When Thurman Thomas made 13 receptions in the Bills' playoff loss to the Browns, whose NFL post-season record did he tie?

●

9   What Bills offensive lineman is a certified basketball and baseball official in Alabama?

●

10 Who scored the first regular-season touchdown for the Bills in a September 18, 1960, game against the Denver Broncos?

•

11 True or false: The Bills' 42–0 rout of the Browns in a 1990 game is the most lopsided victory in Buffalo history.

•

12 In 1975, the Bills traded former No. 1 pick Walt Patulski to the St. Louis Cardinals in exchange for a second-round draft choice.

What offensive lineman did Buffalo choose with that selection?

•

13 What Bill is a deacon at a Lutheran church near Buffalo?

•

14 There was much clamoring among Bills fans before the 1985 draft to select this player rather than Bruce Smith.

•

15 Who is the all-time leading rusher against the Bills?
a) Keith Lincoln
b) Larry Csonka
c) Freeman McNeil
d) Jim Nance

•

16 Who is a member of the Bills Silver Anniversary Team as well as the Giants' all-time leading scorer?

•

17 Scott Norwood kicked a club-tying record 52-yard field goal against the Jets in a September 1991 game. Three other Buffalo kickers have also converted from that distance. Who are they?

•

18 How many times has Jim Kelly completed 60 percent or more of his passes in a season?

•

19 What old-time Bill was Ralph Wilson talking about when he said, "You have to be quite a man to play half of a football game with a broken leg. He was as tough a player as any I've seen"?

The Juice: Now you see him, now you don't. (Buffalo Bills)

A NUMBERS GAME

O.J. Simpson, of course, was No. 32 in your program. But did you know that the Juice also wore two other numbers while playing for the Bills? At his first training camp, in 1969, he was issued 36 because Gary McDermott wouldn't part with 32. The problem was resolved when McDermott was cut before the regular season. O.J. wore his old number for the remainder of his pro football career, with one exception. Before a December 14, 1969, game at San Diego, someone stole Simpson's jersey and he had to make do with No. 33.

Although O.J.'s number hasn't officially been retired, no one has been issued it since Simpson last played for the Bills in 1977.

Another sidenote about the most celebrated number in Buffalo sports history—two Bills, besides Simpson and McDermott, wore No. 32. They were Don Stone in 1965 and Jack Spikes in '66 and '67.

Perhaps the most famous Bills jersey story involves No. 31, now worn by defensive back J.D. Williams. Before Williams was issued the jersey in 1990, only one player had worn the number—Preston Ridlehuber—and that was by mistake. The reserve running back donned No. 31 during an October 11, 1969, game with the old Boston Patriots. Ridlehuber distinguished himself that day when he threw a game-winning 45-yard halfback option pass to Haven Moses. The error was corrected the following week, and Ridlehuber was given No. 36.

Apparently, 31 hadn't been issued in the past because it was the number worn by the generic Buffalo player on letterhead used by the club in the 1960s when the Bills were in the American Football League.

But not all traditions endure, and this one officially ended with Williams's arrival two seasons ago.

Mike Stratton was the author of the most famous hit in Bills history.
(Buffalo Bills)

AN ALL-NUMBERS TEAM

1 - Efren Herrera
2 - Willie Beecher
3 - Pete Gogolak and
 John Leypoldt
4 - John Kidd
5 - Nick Mike-Mayer
6 - Tom Dempsey
7 - Marv Bateman
 and Greg Cater
8 - Stan Gelbaugh
9 - Chris Mohr
10 - Dan Darragh
11 - Scott Norwood
12 - Jim Kelly
13 - Sam Wyche
14 - Frank Reich
15 - Jack Kemp
16 - Dennis Shaw
17 - Warren Rabb
18 - Joe Danelo
19 - Joe Dufek
20 - Joe Cribbs and
 Robert James
21 - Bobby Burnett
22 - Steve Freeman
23 - Kenneth Davis
24 - Booker Edgerson
25 - Roland Hooks and
 Haven Moses
26 - George Saimes
27 - Tom Janik
28 - Greg Bell
29 - Mario Clark
30 - Wray Carlton
31 - J.D. Williams

32 - O.J. Simpson
33 - Ronnie Harmon
34 - Cookie Gilchrist and
 Thurman Thomas
35 - Carl Byrum
36 - Rodney Bellinger
37 - Nate Odomes
38 - Mark Kelso
39 - Jamie Mueller
40 - Robb Riddick
41 - Phil Villapiano
42 - Butch Byrd
43 - Tony Green
44 - Elbert Dubenion
45 - Bill Simpson
46 - Keith Moody
47 - Curtis Brown
48 - Roosevelt Leaks
49 - Booth Lusteg
50 - Al Bemiller
51 - Jim Ritcher
52 - Chris Keating
53 - Will Grant
54 - Eugene Marve
55 - Jim Haslett
56 - Darryl Talley
57 - Lucius Sanford
58 - Shane Conlan and
 Mike Stratton
59 - Shane Nelson
60 - Tom Day
61 - Willie Parker
62 - Ervin Parker
63 - Justin Cross
64 - Harry Jacobs
65 - Tim Vogler

66 - Billy Shaw
67 - Kent Hull and
 Reggie McKenzie
68 - Joe DeLamielleure
69 - Will Wolford
70 - Tom Sestak
71 - Mike Kadish
72 - Ron McDole
73 - Ken Jones
74 - Donnie Green
75 - Howard Ballard
76 - Fred Smerlas
77 - Stew Barber
78 - Bruce Smith
79 - Paul Costa
80 - Jerry Butler
81 - Bob Chandler
82 - Frank Lewis
83 - Andre Reed
84 - Ernie Warlick
85 - Glenn Bass
86 - James Lofton
87 - Paul Seymour and
 Butch Rolle
88 - Pete Metzelaars
89 - Steve Tasker
90 - Tony Hunter
91 - Ken Johnson
92 - Gary Baldinger
93 - Scott Virkus
94 - Mark Pike
95 - Sean McNanie
96 - Leon Seals
97 - Cornelius Bennett
98 - Ira Albright
99 - Hal Garner

20   Match the player with the round in which he was drafted:

Darryl Talley	8th
Jeff Wright	10th
Mike Lodish	4th
Frank Reich	3rd
Leon Seals	2nd

●

21   Name the two members of the Bills' scouting department who were recently enshrined in the Minor League/Semi-Pro Football Hall of Fame.

●

22   Who had more combined yards in his rookie season: Thurman Thomas or Joe Cribbs?

●

23   True or false: Marv Levy was the first full-time special teams coach employed by George Allen.

●

24   Whose fumble during a 1968 game ensured a Bills' loss to Oakland, but on the plus side clinched the No. 1 pick in the draft, which Buffalo used to select O.J. Simpson?

●

25   Who was the only Bills defensive lineman to start all sixteen games in 1991?

●

26   Who has recovered the most fumbles in Bills history?
   a)   Jim Dunaway
   b)   Darryl Talley
   c)   Fred Smerlas
   d)   Harry Jacobs

●

27   How many of Gary Baldinger's brothers have played in the NFL?

●

28   What position did Jim Ritcher originally play with the Bills?

●

29   Name the Bill who was a high school sprint champion in Kansas.

●

30   Who caught the winning touchdown pass in the Bills' 47–41 shoot-out victory against the Oilers in a 1989 game in the Houston Astrodome?

31 Who said: "There's nothing I hate more than missing a tackle. It's like popping up in baseball"?

32 Name the three Bills who have been featured on the cover of *Sports Illustrated.*

33 True or false: Pittsburgh's famed Steel Curtain defense registered a league-leading 52 sacks during the 1974 season, but failed to get to the Bills quarterbacks at all in their 32–14 playoff victory against Buffalo that year.

34 Match the Bill with his pastime:

Thurman Thomas   Weight lifting
Leonard Smith   Collecting Garfield dolls
Walt Corey   Playing keyboards
Butch Rolle   Restoring old cars

35 Where was the Bills' first training camp held?

36 Who was Ralph Wilson referring to when he said: "The guy's unflappable. He's a great insurance policy"?
   a) Daryle Lamonica
   b) Frank Reich
   c) Ed Rutkowski
   d) Marlin Briscoe

37 How many turnovers did the Bills commit in Super Bowl XXVI?
   a) 5
   b) 6
   c) 7
   d) 8

38 Only four receivers in Bills history have surpassed 1,000 yards in a season. Name them.

39 What NFL team originally drafted Chris Mohr?

A HERO OF TWO FIELDS

On a wall outside the lobby at Rich Stadium hangs a plaque with a picture of a young man in his twenties wearing a Bills uniform. There is an old Bills helmet, the white one with the standing red Buffalo, to the left of the plaque and a camouflaged Army helmet to the right. Below it, there is a metal etching of the man's name, taken from Vietnam Veterans Memorial in Washington, D.C., along with three notes from the man's adoring wife and children.

The shrine is dedicated to Bob Kalsu, the Bills offensive tackle who was killed on a jungle mountaintop in Vietnam on July 21, 1970. He was the only active National Football League player to die in the war.

The Bills had selected him out of the University of Oklahoma in the eighth round of the 1968 draft. Kalsu broke into the starting lineup immediately and was named Buffalo's rookie of the year. The Army came calling the following season, and Kalsu, a former ROTC student, was sent to Fort Still at Lawton, Oklahoma. While his teammates prepared for the 1969 season, Kalsu was shipped out to Vietnam as a second lieutenant in the 101st Screaming Eagles airborne division.

Less than a year later he and several others were killed when mortar fire rained down on Firebase Ripcord.

40 What team released James Lofton?

•

41 Name the three backs who have led the Bills in rushing and receiving in the same season.

•

42 Bill Polian and this Bills assistant coach once worked together on the Columbia University football staff.

•

43 True or false: O.J. Simpson had a better yards-per-game average during his 2,000-yard rushing season than Eric Dickerson had when he broke the Juice's record a decade later.

•

44 What was the halftime score of the Bills–Raiders championship game?

•

45 What two motorcycle-riding offensive linemen are known as "The Harley Boys?"

•

46 Who was the original Voice of the Bills?
   a) Rick Azar
   b) Van Miller
   c) John Murphy
   d) Al Meltzer

•

47 Who leads the Bills in post-season interceptions?
   a) Butch Byrd
   b) Darryl Talley
   c) Bill Simpson
   d) Mark Kelso

•

48 True or false: Jim Kelly threw as many touchdown passes in Super Bowl XXVI as his Washington counterpart, Mark Rypien.

•

49 How many career interceptions did Carlton Bailey have before the one he made against John Elway in the AFC title game against the Denver Broncos?

•

50 Does former Bills coach Chuck Knox have a winning record against Buffalo?

Bob Kalsu, an offensive lineman with tremendous promise, was the only active NFL player killed during the Vietnam War. (Courtesy of Pete Knaus)

THE GREAT DEBATE: THOMAS OR SANDERS?

When they were teammates at Oklahoma State, there was no debate about who was better. Thurman Thomas was the starting running back, the man who carried the load, and Barry Sanders was his understudy. It wasn't until Thomas was drafted by the Bills in 1988 and Sanders was winning the Heisman Trophy by a landslide that same year that the arguments started. The debate has become more heated now that each is an NFL megastar. The arguments go something like this: Barry's the superior runner, the guy with more moves than North American Van Lines, but Thurman's the better all-around player, the back of all trades, who can hurt you whether he's running with the ball or catching it. So who's better? Depends whether you like apples or oranges. The bottom line is you wouldn't lose with either one of these guys in your backfield. Realizing that numbers tell only part of the story, here's a statistical comparison of the onetime college teammates:

Thurman Thomas   Barry Sanders

COLLEGE

Totals	Rushing	Receiving	TDs	Totals	Rushing	Receiving	TDs
4 years	4,595	598	45	3 years	3,556	411	48

PRO

Year	Rushing	Receiving	TDs	Year	Rushing	Receiving	TDs
1988	881	208	2	1989	1,470	282	14
1989	1,244	669	12	1990	1,304	462	16
1990	1,297	532	13	1991	1,548	307	18
Totals	3,422	1,409	27	Totals	4,322	1,051	48

1. Jim Kelly and Chris Mohr.
2. (b) Thurman Thomas. He rushed for 165 yards on 25 carries and caught eight passes for 103 yards in the '91 season opener against Miami.
3. True. Kelly has completed 60.6 percent of his passes, second only to Joe Montana's 63.6 percent.
4. (c) Joe Devlin. He tops the list with 197 games, 10 more than Jim Ritcher entering the '92 season.
5. Tommy O'Connell.
6. (a) Cookie Gilchrist scored 30 points on five touchdowns in a December 8, 1963, game against the New York Jets.
7. 1988 and '90. In '88, they went 9–0, while in '90 they went 10–0.
8. Kellen Winslow's. The former San Diego Chargers great caught 13 passes in a 1981 playoff game against the Miami Dolphins.
9. Howard Ballard.
10. Wray Carlton on a 1-yard run.
11. False. The Bills' 48-point win against the Raiders in the AFC title game is Buffalo's most decisive victory.
12. Joe Devlin.
13. Steve Tasker.
14. Doug Flutie.
15. (c) Freeman McNeil. The former Jet amassed 830 yards during his career against Buffalo.
16. Pete Gogolak.
17. Joe Danelo, John Leypoldt, Grant Guthrie.
18. Twice. In 1990, he completed 63.29 percent, while the following season he improved to 64.1 percent.
19. Tom Sestak.
20. Talley (2nd); Wright (8th); Lodish (10th); Reich (3rd); Seals (4th).
21. A.J. Smith and Bob Windish.
22. Joe Cribbs had 1,600 yards rushing and receiving compared with 1,089 for Thomas.
23. False. Dick Vermeil was the first with Allen's Rams in 1969. He left after a year and Allen replaced him with Levy.
24. Ed Rutkowski's fumble prevented the Bills from beating the Raiders. Had Buffalo won, they would have had a better record than Philadelphia, and the Eagles presumably

would have chosen Simpson instead of Purdue's Leroy Keyes.

25. Leon Seals.
26. (a) Jim Dunaway has the most recoveries with 12.
27. Two: Brian with the Colts and Rich with the Chiefs.
28. Center.
29. Steve Tasker.
30. Andre Reed.
31. Shane Conlan.
32. O.J. Simpson, Bruce Smith, and Thurman Thomas. Jim Kelly has also appeared on the cover of *SI,* but in a New Jersey Generals uniform two months before signing with the Bills.
33. True.
34. Thomas (collecting Garfield dolls); Smith (restoring old cars); Corey (weightlifting); Rolle (playing keyboards).
35. Roycroft Inn in East Aurora.
36. (b) Frank Reich
37. (d) 8—four interceptions and four fumbles.
38. Andre Reed, Frank Lewis, Marlin Briscoe, and James Lofton.
39. Tampa Bay in the sixth round of the 1989 draft.
40. Los Angeles Raiders.
41. Keith Lincoln in 1967, Joe Cribbs in 1983, and Greg Bell in 1985.
42. Tom Bresnahan.
43. True. O.J. averaged 143 yards per game, while Dickerson averaged 132.
44. The Bills led 41–3.
45. Mitch Frerotte and Glenn Parker.
46. (b) Van Miller
47. (d) Mark Kelso with four.
48. True.
49. One.
50. Yes. Knox is 3–1 against his former employer—1–0 with the Rams, and 2–1 with the Seahawks.

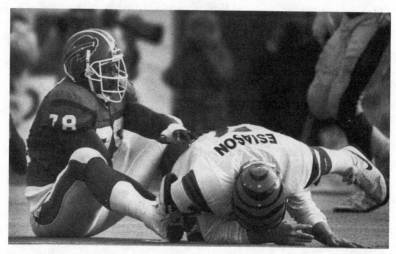

Bruce Smith, the Bills' all-time sack leader with 78, lowers the boom on Boomer Esiason. (Jamie Germano/Gannett Rochester Newspapers)

FOURTH
QUARTER

FOURTH QUARTER—QUESTIONS

1   True or false: The Bills' no-name offensive line actually weighs more than the Washington Redskins' celebrated Hogs.

•

2   How many running backs were chosen in the 1988 draft before Thurman Thomas? For bonus points, name them.

•

3   Who said: "I sprint down the field with an aura of invincibility. Nobody is going to stop me. I'm going to make the play. I don't care about my wife, my kids, my dog, my house. Nothing. With 60 yards to wind up, I know it's going to be an incredible collision. It sounds absolutely barbaric to say, but laying a good lick on somebody is the best feeling ever"?

•

4   What team snapped the Bills' club-record 17-game home winning streak?

•

5   When Al Edwards returned a kickoff 91 yards for a touchdown against the Raiders in a 1991 game, it marked the first time in thirteen years that a Bill had taken a kickoff the distance. Who was the last Buffalo player to return a kickoff for a touchdown?

•

6   These two free agent acquisitions accounted for five of the Bills' seven touchdowns in their championship rout of the Raiders.

•

7   Whose Super Bowl record did Jim Kelly eclipse when he put the ball up 58 times against the Redskins?
    a) Dan Marino's
    b) Joe Montana's
    c) Terry Bradshaw's
    d) John Elway's

•

8   What Bill has a commercial pilot's license and would like to fly the friendly skies when he's through playing football?

•

9   True or false: Bruce Smith has never led the NFL in sacks.

•

10 Match the Bills coach with his alma mater:

Elijah Pitts   Miami, Florida
Walt Corey   Black Hills State
Tom Bresnahan   Philander Smith College
Dick Roach   Holy Cross

●

11 Did Marv Levy have a winning record against the Bills when he was coaching Kansas City?

●

12 Who gave Howard Ballard the nickname "House"? (Hint: It was a player and a former assistant coach.)

●

13 Name the six Bills starters that came out of the 1987 draft.

●

14 True or false: No Bills quarterback has thrown for 400 yards in a regular-season game.

●

15 Who has scored the most points against the Bills through the years?
   a) Gino Cappelletti
   b) Garo Yapremian
   c) Pat Leahy
   d) Jan Stenerud

●

16 Name the only defensive backs in Bills history to intercept 10 passes in a single season.

●

17 To whom was Thurman Thomas referring when he said, following a 30–27 overtime victory against the Raiders in 1991, "If he would have missed that one, I would have dropped him from the plane over Minnesota or North Dakota"?

●

18 This Pro Bowl offensive lineman began his high school career as a quarterback.
   a) Jim Ritcher
   b) Joe DeLamielleure
   c) Kent Hull
   d) Will Wolford

●

19 Which Bills running back has the most career receptions?
   a) Joe Cribbs   c) O.J. Simpson
   b) Robb Riddick   d) Thurman Thomas

71

20 From February 1991 through Super Bowl XXVI, this player participated in 34 professional football games.

21 True or false: O.J. Simpson gained 100 yards in his only playoff appearance.

22 In which decade (discounting the '90s) have the Bills enjoyed their greatest success?

23 In 1989, he became the first NFL player to wear a "Gazoo" helmet, a protective covering that reduces the risk of concussions.

24 This Bills cornerback finished second in the Big Ten long jump competition as a senior.

25 What Bill finished fifth in the 1984 Heisman Trophy balloting?

26 Who is the Bills all-time post-season scoring leader?
   a)   Thurman Thomas
   b)   Andre Reed
   c)   Pete Gogolak
   d)   Scott Norwood

27 What former Bills draft choice now starts in the Washington Redskins secondary?

28 Who scored the only touchdown in the Bills 31–7 loss to the Chiefs in the 1966 AFL title game?

29 True or false: Marv Levy has the longest continuous run of any Bills head coach.

30 With which AFL team did Paul Maguire begin his professional football career?
   a)   Buffalo Bills
   b)   Kansas City Chiefs
   c)   Los Angeles Chargers
   d)   Boston Patriots

STRANGE BUT TRUE

Ralph Wilson has bred horses and Butch Rolle has two pet boa constrictors, but when it comes to Bills animal lovers, no one can top Joe Auer, a reserve halfback for the 1964–65 teams. While at Georgia Tech, Auer had a pet lion cub and alligator in his dorm room. This didn't set well with school officials who eventually told Auer: "Either they go or you go." They went. The alligator died and Auer donated the lion to a circus. When he joined the Bills, Auer bred quarter horses, which certainly must have earned him a brownie point or two with his boss.

•

Mitch Frerotte, the war-paint wearing, motorcycle-driving reserve offensive lineman, said he has been contacted by the World Wrestling Federation about becoming a professional grappler once his Bills days are through. Frerotte said he would use his football nickname, Pit Bull. "I intend to be a bad guy because there are no rules for bad guys," said Frerotte.

•

If there was a vote for ugliest game in Bills history, Buffalo's 6–3 overtime victory against the Giants during the 1987 strike probably would win in a landslide. Marv Levy remembers the game well, especially the performance of center Will Grant, who had been coaxed out of retirement to block Lawrence Taylor.
"Will got six holding penalties in the first half," Levy recalled. "I talked to him at halftime. I said, "Will, you've got six holding penalties." He said, "For the amount of time I've been holding, that's good."

•

During the early 1960s while attending one of his players' weddings, Ralph Wilson was introduced to George Saimes, who had been drafted by the Kansas City Chiefs. During their conversation, Saimes mentioned that he would love to play for the Bills, so before the season, Wilson engineered a trade that made Saimes's wish come true. It proved to be a great trade.

Saimes, a strong safety, is a member of the Bills All-Time Team.

●

A few days before Super Bowl XXV, Bills linebacker Cornelius Bennett told reporters: "I hope we win by a big margin or really lose by a big margin. I don't want to lose it in the waning seconds of the game because that would be awfully hard to swallow, to lose like that."

A day later, former Bills and Giants kicker Pete Gogolak said: "All I'm going to say is it will be a close game. It will come down to a field goal."

Bennett's worst fears came true and Gogolak's words proved prophetic as it came down to a field goal, a missed field goal by Scott Norwood in the final seconds.

●

Speaking of missed field goals, former Bills kicker Booth Lusteg botched a 23-yarder in the closing seconds of a 1966 game against the San Diego Chargers and the game ended in a 17–17 tie. On his walk home from War Memorial Stadium, a group of teenagers beat up Lusteg. When police later asked him why he hadn't called for help, Lusteg said, "Because I deserved it."

●

Rich Stadium is notorious for its unpredictable winds, but the old Rockpile was no day at the beach either, according to Gogolak. "There was this one time I kicked a field goal there and when I came off the field, my foot was killing me," he recalled of War Memorial Stadium. "Afterwards, the groundskeeper discovered the cause of my pain. My foot had banged against a part of a Coke bottle that was sticking out of the ground."

●

Like mother, like son. Marvcus Patton isn't the first to play linebacker in his family. His mother, Barbara, played for the Los Angeles Dandelions of the Women's Professional Football League. Her $25-a-game salary was nowhere close to the six-figure contract her son is pulling down with the Bills. These days, she keeps a coachly eye on her son. She's not afraid to dole out advice.

"Sometimes he tells me, 'Yeah, yeah, I know, Mom. I'm a pro football player,'" she recalled. "I say, 'Don't forget I was one, too.'"

31   Who was the only rookie to start for the Bills in 1991?

32   Match the player with his alma mater:

John Davis	UCLA
Marvcus Patton	Georgia Tech
James Lofton	Utah State
Hal Garner	Stanford

33   Which Bills quarterback has the best post-season won-lost record—Jim Kelly, Jack Kemp, or Joe Ferguson?

34   True or false: The Bills are the only team to have won four straight AFC East titles.

35   What Bill beat out Heisman Trophy–winner Mike Garrett of the Chiefs for AFL Rookie-of-the-Year honors in 1966?
   a)   Bobby Burnett
   b)   Cookie Gilchrist
   c)   Wray Carlton
   d)   Art Baker

36   What Bill helped lead Booker T. Washington's basketball team to the Virginia scholastic basketball championship?

37   What is Jim Kelly's middle name?

38   Who was the first person to purchase a Bills season ticket?
   a)   Buster Ramsey
   b)   Ernie Warlick
   c)   Archie Diemer
   d)   Jack Kemp

39   True or false: Mark Rypien failed to throw for 300 yards, and no Redskins running back gained 100 yards in Super Bowl XXVI.

40   This Bills Pro Bowler joined the team the same day as Jim Kelly.

41   Everyone knows that Scott Norwood missed from 47 yards

in Super Bowl XXV. But earlier in the game he made a field goal. How long was it?

●

42 What was Bill Polian's official position when he joined the Bills in 1984?
   a) General Manager
   b) Assistant GM
   c) Scout
   d) Director of Pro Personnel

●

43 How many times has Jim Kelly been selected to the Pro Bowl?

●

44 How many of Levy's current assistants worked for him in Kansas City?

●

45 True or false: The Bills have a winning record at home.

●

46 Name the two Bills to have been named NFL Most Valuable Player by the Associated Press.

●

47 Who scored the Bills' first regular-season touchdown at Rich Stadium?

●

48 What two players share the club record for most receptions in a regular-season game?

●

49 Who has more catches in the post-season—Andre Reed or Thurman Thomas?

●

50 True or false: The Bills have a winning record against each AFC East team except the Dolphins.

FEELING A DRAFT

When times are good, as they are now for Buffalo, you can trace much of the success to shrewd drafting. And when times are bad, it's usually an indication that those weren't diamonds in the rough the scouts prospected, but rather pieces of coal. Here's a look at some Bills drafts to remember, and forget.

BLUE CHIPS

1979—Funny how things work out. The first Bills pick was Tom Cousineau. He, of course, snubbed Buffalo for the Canadian Football League, and the fans were all over Ralph Wilson for being a tightwad. In retrospect, not signing Cousineau turned out to be one of the best things to happen to the Bills. Buffalo eventually traded the rights to Cousineau in exchange for a first-round draft pick, which it used to select Jim Kelly in 1983. But even if Buffalo had received nothing for Cousineau (who, by the way, turned out to be a big bust), this still would have ranked as the Bills' best draft. Norm Pollom's scouting department discovered seven starters in this crop—Fred Smerlas, Jerry Butler, Jim Haslett, Jon Borchardt, Ken Johnson, Jeff Nixon, and Rod Kush.

1987—This also was a kick-butt draft with six choices who eventually became starters: Shane Conlan, Nate Odomes, Keith McKeller, Leon Seals, Howard Ballard, and Jamie Mueller.

1985—This one laid the foundation for Buffalo's current revival. It produced four starters (Bruce Smith, Andre Reed, Derrick Burroughs, and Chris Burkett) and two important backups (Frank Reich and Hal Garner).

1961—In this draft, the Bills discovered three offensive lineman—Billy Shaw, Stew Barber, and Al Bemiller—who would play major roles on their championship teams in the mid-1960s.

1966—The first three picks were Mike Dennis, Jim Lindsey, and Randy Jackson. Never heard of them? That's understandable. None of them made the team.

1975—Roland Hooks, a tenth-rounder, was the only pick to distinguish himself; that's how bad this crop was.

1965—Jim Davidson in the first round. Nobody in the second. Alan Atkinson in the third. Need we say more?

1982—This will forever be remembered as the Perry Tuttle draft. Pollom wanted the Bills to choose wide receiver Mike Quick, but Coach Chuck Knox was insistent on selecting Tuttle, the nation's top-rated receiver. So the Bills took Tuttle, who played a couple of forgettable seasons before being cut, while the Philadelphia Eagles got stuck with Quick, who wound up making the Pro Bowl a zillion years in a row.

1. True. With John Davis in the lineup, the Bills weigh 1,452 pounds. With Glenn Parker they tip the scales at 1,469. Either way that tops the Hogs' total of 1,448 pounds.
2. Seven. Brad Muster, Lorenzo White, Gaston Green, John Stephens, Ironhead Heyward, Ickey Woods, and Tony Jeffrey.
3. Steve Tasker.
4. The Detroit Lions.
5. Curtis Brown returned a kickoff 102 yards for a touchdown against Baltimore in 1978.
6. Kenneth Davis (3) and James Lofton (2).
7. (a) Dan Marino's
8. Jim Ritcher.
9. True, though he did come close in 1990 when he finished second, just one behind Kansas City's Derrick Thomas, who had 20.
10. Pitts (Philander Smith); Corey (Miami, Florida); Bresnahan (Holy Cross); Roach (Black Hills State).
11. No. Levy's Chiefs lost two of three games against the Bills.
12. Cornelius Bennett and former Bills defensive line coach Ted Cottrell.
13. Linebacker Shane Conlan, cornerback Nate Odomes, fullback Jamie Mueller, defensive end Leon Seals, tight end Keith McKeller, and offensive tackle Howard Ballard.
14. False. Joe Ferguson passed for a club-record 419 yards in the Bills' 38–35 overtime victory against the Miami Dolphins in 1983.
15. (c) Pat Leahy with 163 career points.
16. Billy Atkins in 1961 and Tom Janik in 1967.
17. Kicker Scott Norwood, who had had a rough day, missing an extra point and three field goal attempts before booting the game-winner in overtime.
18. (c) Kent Hull.
19. (d) Thurman Thomas with 189.
20. Chris Mohr. He punted in fifteen games with the Montreal Machine of the WLAF and nineteen games for the Bills.
21. False. The Juice was limited to 49 yards on 15 carries in the Bills' 32–14 loss to the Pittsburgh Steelers on December 27, 1974.
22. The '60s was by far their finest decade, even though they finished the ten-year period below .500. The Bills were 65-

69-6 in the '60s; 51-91-2 in the '70s; and 69–83 in the '80s. They are off to a good start in the '90s with a 26–6 record and consecutive trips to the Super Bowl.

23. Mark Kelso.

24. Nate Odomes.

25. Kenneth Davis while playing for Texas Christian University.

26. (d) Scott Norwood with 66 points.

27. Martin Mayhew.

28. Elbert Dubenion on a 69-yard pass from Jack Kemp.

29. True. Levy has been at the job for 5½ seasons, breaking the longevity record previously held by Chuck Knox, who coached the Bills from 1978 to '82.

30. (c) Los Angeles Chargers

31. Defensive end Phil Hansen. He started ten games in place of injured Bruce Smith.

32. Davis (Georgia Tech); Patton (UCLA); Lofton (Stanford); Garner (Utah State).

33. Kelly is 5–4 in the post-season, followed by Kemp's 2–2 and Fergy's 1–3.

34. False. In fact, the Dolphins have done it three times. They won six in a row (1973–78) once and four in row twice (1971–74 and 1981–85).

35. (a) Bobby Burnett.

36. Bruce Smith.

37. Edward.

38. (c) Archie Diemer was first in line on February 8, 1960, when the tickets went on sale at Buffalo's Statler-Hilton.

39. True. Rypien threw for 292 yards and Ricky Ervins led Washington rushers with 72 yards.

40. Kent Hull.

41. 23 yards.

42. (d) Director of Pro Personnel.

43. Four.

44. Four.

45. True. The Bills are 122-111-4 (127-113-4 if you count play-offs) at home. They are 91-138-4 (93-145-4) on the road.

46. O.J. Simpson in 1973 and Thurman Thomas in 1991.

47. Wallace Francis on a 101-yard kickoff return in an October 7, 1973, game against the Philadelphia Eagles.

48. Andre Reed and Greg Bell with 13 apiece.

49. Reed has 42, five more than Thomas.

50. False. The Bills have winning records against the Jets and Colts, but losing ones against the Dolphins and Patriots.

OVERTIME

1   The Bills were 15–48 in the four years before this player's arrival and have gone 47–17 with two Super Bowls in the four years since. Name this impact player.

●

2   Who is the Bills' good-luck national anthem singer?

●

3   Who said: "When I try to take on the wedge it's like throwing a marshmallow at a steamroller"?

●

4   This well-known film critic once had Marv Levy as a camp counselor.

●

5   True or false: Since coming into the National Football League in 1985, Bruce Smith has more sacks than Lawrence Taylor.

●

6   James Lofton entered the 1992 season as the fourth-leading pass-catcher in NFL history, with 699 receptions. What three players ranked ahead of him?

●

7   Match the former Bill with his alma mater:

Bobby Chandler	Millersville (Pennsylvania) State
Pete Gogolak	Nebraska
John Kidd	USC
Robb Riddick	Cornell
Ron McDole	Northwestern

●

8   How many general managers have there been in Bills history?
   a) 10
   b) 6
   c) 9
   d) 3

●

9   Name the six Bills to have rushed for 1,000 yards in a single season.

●

10   True or false: Ralph Wilson has bred two horses that have run in the Kentucky Derby.

11 Which quarterback holds the record for most passing yards in a single game against the Bills?
   a) George Blanda
   b) Gary Hogeboom
   c) Daryle Lamonica
   d) Dan Marino

12 What tattoo-bearing Bill said: "They're addictive. Once you have one done, you want more"?

13 Who is the Bills' all-time leader in 100-yard receiving games?
   a) Jerry Butler
   b) Frank Lewis
   c) Elbert Dubenion
   d) Andre Reed

14 How many quarterbacks went down with injuries before Ed Rutkowski got an opportunity to play during the 1968 season?

15 This Bills assistant led the Southwestern (Kansas) College basketball team in scoring two straight years.

16 True or false: Jim Kelly didn't have a touchdown pass or an interception in Super Bowl XXV.

17 Which two players tied for the team lead in interceptions in 1991?
   a) Mark Kelso and Nate Odomes
   b) Nate Odomes and Darryl Talley
   c) Darryl Talley and Kirby Jackson
   d) Kirby Jackson and Leonard Smith

18 When did Ted Marchibroda first begin thinking about the no-huddle?

19 How many plays did Thurman Thomas miss in Super Bowl XXVI after misplacing his helmet?

IT AIN'T OVER 'TIL IT'S OVER

Here's a look at ten Bills comebacks worth replaying:

Bills 45, Denver 38. Bears Stadium. October 28, 1962. The visiting Bills trailed 38–23 with 11:57 remaining, but stormed back behind quarterback Warren Rabb, who threw TD passes of 75 and 40 yards, scored on a two-point conversion, and also ran the ball in from the four for the winning touchdown.

Bills 20, New England 17. Rich Stadium. November 22, 1981. With only 35 seconds remaining, the Bills drove 73 yards in two plays and won the game when Joe Ferguson's Hail Mary pass was deflected into the arms of Roland Hooks.

Bills 23, Rams 20. Rich Stadium. October 16, 1989. Jim Kelly was sidelined with a separated shoulder, but Frank proved he had—as one banner suggested— "The Reich Stuff," throwing two touchdown passes in the final two minutes and 23 seconds to lead the underdog Bills to a stunning upset on "Monday Night Football."

Bills 29, Denver 28. Rich Stadium. September 30, 1990. Seventy-seven seconds. That's how long it took the Bills to score 20 points and wipe out a 21–9 fourth-quarter deficit. Nate Odomes started things when he blocked a David Treadwell field goal and Cornelius Bennett returned it 80 yards for a TD. On Denver's next possession, Leon Seals tipped a John Elway pass and Leonard Smith sprinted with it 39 yards for a score. Elway then lost the handle on a snap and Bennett recovered at the Broncos two, setting up a Kenneth Davis touchdown.

Bills 38, Raiders 24. Rich Stadium. October 7, 1990. The Bills trailed by three midway through the final quarter when Steve Tasker blocked a Jeff Gossett punt and J.D. Williams returned it 38 yards for the go-ahead score. Two plays later, Bennett caused a fumble, setting up a 23-yard field goal by Scott Norwood. Moments later, Odomes literally stole the ball from receiver Willie Gault and raced 49 yards for a touchdown.

Bills 27, Miami 24. Joe Robbie Stadium, Miami. September 10, 1989. Jim Kelly, who'll never be mistaken for Carl Lewis, ran it in from the two as time expired, capping a comeback from an 11-point deficit with about four minutes remaining.

Bills 20, New York Jets 17. War Memorial Stadium. September 10, 1967. Buffalo scored 20 straight points in the fourth quarter. Mike Mercer, who was making his Bills debut, kicked the winning field goal.

Bills 38, Miami 35. (Overtime.) Orange Bowl, Miami. October 9, 1983. Joe Ferguson completed 38 passes for 419 yards and Joe Danelo kicked the winning field goal to spoil the NFL debut of Dan Marino and Mark Duper.

Bills 34, Miami 31. (Overtime.) Joe Robbie Stadium, Miami. October 25, 1987. The Bills battled back from a 21–0 deficit as Kelly completed 18 of 23 passes for 244 yards and two touchdowns in the second half and Robb Riddick scored three touchdowns. Scott Norwood's 27-yard field goal 4:12 into overtime decided it.

Bills 21, Oakland 20. Rich Stadium. September 16, 1974. Buffalo pulled out the Monday-night victory on Joe Ferguson's 31-yard scoring pass to Ahmad Rashad with 26 seconds remaining.

20 True or false: Bills longsnapper Adam Lingner's radio show in Buffalo was sponsored, in part, by Snapper Tools.

21 How many sacks did the Bills get against the Hogs in Super Bowl XXVI?

22 This Bills receiver was a three-time track-and-field All-American and once recorded the world's longest long jump.
  a) Jerry Butler
  b) James Lofton
  c) Bobby Chandler
  d) Ahmad Rashad

23 True or false: At the first AFL draft, Ralph Wilson did the selecting with counseling from several college coaches he respected.

24 What's the most common surname among players in Bills history?
  a) Johnson
  b) Jones
  c) Smith
  d) Williams

25 True or false: Scott Norwood is the sixth most accurate field goal kicker in NFL history.

26 What Bill is known to his teammates as "Squatty Body"?

27 What former Bills assistant coach spent his spare time doing macramé?

28 What Bill won the Vince Lombardi Award during his senior season, becoming the first linebacker to receive the honor?
  a) Shane Conlan
  b) Darryl Talley
  c) Carlton Bailey
  d) Cornelius Bennett

29 Upon whose recommendation did the Bills hire Bill Polian in 1984?

Jim Kelly knows a thing or two about comebacks. (Jamie Germano/Gannett Rochester Newspapers)

30 What game was Marv Levy referring to when he said: "I remember it well. I'll remember it all my life. I think it was the worst game ever played in the National Football League"?

31 In 1990, Jim Kelly became the fifth quarterback to compile a passing efficiency rating above 100. What other quarterbacks have accomplished the feat?

32 True or false: Opponents have returned only one kickoff or punt for a touchdown since Bruce DeHaven became the Bills' special teams coach in 1987.

33 This former Bills punter's father is a longtime NBA referee.
a) John Kidd
b) Rick Tuten
c) John Nies
d) Greg Cater

34 Which ex-Bill has two boa constrictors as pets?

35 How many yards did Thurman Thomas gain during his big "Monday Night" performance against the Jets in 1990?
a) 204
b) 214
c) 224
d) 234

36 Mark Kelso has 23 career interceptions tying him with two others for fifth place on the club's All-time list. With which former Bill does he share the No. 5 spot?

37 Scott Norwood has attempted ten field goals of 50 or more yards in his career. How many has he made?

38 Where did Bills Assistant General Manager Bob Ferguson play his college football?

39 True or false: The Bills were the first AFL team to officially draft former Syracuse University Heisman Trophy–winner Ernie Davis.

40 Match the No. 1 draft pick with the year he was selected:

O.J. Simpson	1972
Bruce Smith	1979
Tom Cousineau	1969
Walt Patulski	1985

●

41 Andre Reed (1,113) and James Lofton (1,072) each topped the 1,000-yard receiving mark in 1991. Has any other Bills receiving tandem accomplished the feat?

●

42 This former Colts and Dolphins great was Jim Kelly's quarterbacks coach at the University of Miami.

●

43 Who was James Lofton's head coach during his senior year at Stanford University?

●

44 True or false: The Bills have never lost a playoff game in Rich Stadium.

●

45 Who holds the Bills record for best kickoff return average in a season?
   a) O.J. Simpson
   b) Charley Warner
   c) Keith Moody
   d) Ed Rutkowski

●

46 Who are the only two Bills to amass 2,000 yards from scrimmage in a single season?

●

47 Who finished second on the Bills in sacks in 1992?
   a) Jeff Wright   c) Leonard Smith
   b) Darryl Talley   d) Shane Conlan

●

48 Name the Bill who was named to the Pro Bowl for an eighth time in 1991.

●

49 True or false: Jim Kelly has thrown more touchdown passes than interceptions in post-season play.

●

50 Name the three Bills chosen to the All-time AFL team.

Lou Saban: The coach with the most wins in Bills history. (Buffalo Bills)

MORE TRAVELS WITH LOU

Since our last trivia book, nomadic Lou Saban has added three more jobs to his busy résumé. In the past 42 years, the Marco Polo of coaching has held 23 positions. Here's an update:

1992	Assistant football coach, Tampa Bay Storm, Arena Football League.
1991	Head football coach, Peru (Nebraska) State College.
1990	Head football coach, Middle Georgia Heatwave in the Minor League football system.
1989	Head football coach, Georgetown (South Carolina) High School.
1988	Head football coach, South Fork (Florida), High School.
1986–87	Assistant football coach, Martin County (Stuart, Florida).
1984–86	Scout, New York Yankees.
1983–84	Head coach, Central Florida University.
1980–82	President, New York Yankees.
1979	Head football coach, U.S. Military Academy.
1977–78	Head football coach, University of Miami, (Florida).
1976	Athletic Director, University of Cincinnati.
1972–76	Head football coach, Buffalo Bills, NFL.
1967–71	Head football coach, Denver Broncos, NFL.
1966	Head football coach, University of Maryland.
1962–65	Head football coach, Buffalo Bills, AFL.
1960–61	Head football coach, Boston Patriots, AFL.
1957–59	Head football coach, Western Illinois University.
1956	Insurance salesman.
1954–55	Assistant and head football coach, Northwestern University.
1953	Assistant football coach, University of Washington.
1950–52	Head football coach, Case Institute of Technology.

THE LEADERS

PASSING

Name	Years	Att.	Comp.	Yards	Pct.	TDs	Int.
Joe Ferguson	1973–84	4,166	2,188	27,590	52.5	181	190
Jim Kelly	1986–	2,562	1,555	19,574	60.7	138	89
Jack Kemp	1962–69	2,240	1,040	15,138	46.4	77	132
Dennis Shaw	1970–73	916	485	6,286	52.9	35	67
John Green	1960–61	354	145	2,170	41.0	16	15
Daryle Lamonica	1963–66	353	150	2,499	42.5	16	23
Dan Darragh	1968–70	296	127	1,353	42.9	4	22
Vince Ferragamo	1985	287	149	1,677	51.9	5	17
Gary Marangi	1974–76	283	104	1,373	36.7	12	21
Warren Rabb	1961–62	251	101	1,782	40.2	15	16

RUSHING

Name	Years	Att.	Yards	Avg.	TDs
O.J. Simpson	1969–77	2,123	10,183	4.8	57
Thurman Thomas	1988–	1,064	4,829	4.5	26
Joe Cribbs	1980–83, '85	1,082	4,445	4.1	21
Wray Carlton	1960–67	819	3,368	4.1	29
Cookie Gilchrist	1962–64	676	3,056	4.5	31
Jim Braxton	1971–78	721	2,842	3.9	23
Greg Bell	1984–87	589	2,420	4.1	19
Curtis Brown	1977–82	564	2,171	3.9	8
Roland Hooks	1976–82	399	1,682	4.2	12
Terry Miller	1978–80	389	1,579	4.1	8

RECEIVING

Name	Years	Rec.	Yards	Avg.	TDs
Andre Reed	1985–	467	6,435	13.8	48
Elbert Dubenion	1960–68	296	5,309	17.9	35
Bob Chandler	1971–79	295	3,999	13.6	34
Jerry Butler	1979–86	278	4,301	15.5	29
Frank Lewis	1978–83	269	4,638	17.2	24
Thurman Thomas	1988–	189	2,040	10.8	13
Joe Cribbs	1980–83 '85	180	1,783	9.9	15
O.J. Simpson	1969–77	175	1,924	11.0	12
Glen Bass	1961–66	162	2,799	17.3	16
J.D. Hill	1971–75	160	2,631	16.4	20

OVERTIME—ANSWERS

1. Thurman Thomas.
2. Sharon Jones, wife of Bills' strength and conditioning coach, Rusty. Buffalo is 14–2 in games in which Sharon has sung the national anthem.
3. Steve Tasker.
4. Gene Siskel of Siskel and Ebert fame.
5. False. Since 1985, Smith's rookie year, he has 78 sacks compared to 94 for L.T.
6. Steve Largent (819), Art Monk (801), and Charlie Joiner (750).
7. Chandler (USC); Gogolak (Cornell); Kidd (Northwestern); Riddick (Millersville State); McDole (Nebraska).
8. (b) Six. Dick Gallagher (1960–66); Bob Lustig (1967–78); Stew Barber (1979–82); Patrick McGroder (1983); Terry Bledsoe (1984–85); Bill Polian (1986–91).
9. Cookie Gilchrist, O.J. Simpson, Terry Miller, Joe Cribbs, Greg Bell, Thurman Thomas.
10. True. Pat McGroder ran at Churchill Downs in the 1974 Derby, and Arazi, whom Wilson bred but sold, finished sixth in the 1992 Derby.
11. (a) Blanda. He had 464 passing yards in a 1961 game against the Bills.
12. Glenn Parker.
13. (d) Reed. He had 19 entering the 1992 season.
14. Five. Jack Kemp, Tom Flores, Dan Darragh, Ben Russell, and Kay Stephenson.
15. Bruce DeHaven.
16. True.
17. (b) Odomes and Talley with five apiece.
18. Way back in 1961 when he was an assistant coach with the Washington Redskins. Marchibroda recalls riding to work with several assistants when one of the coaches suggested that one day all plays would be called at the line of scrimmage and the huddle would become obsolete. Marchibroda filed the idea away, and 30 years later, the offense of the '90s was unveiled.
19. Two.
20. Strange but true.
21. Zero.

22. (b) James Lofton. He accomplished those feats while at Stanford University.
23. True. The Bills had been granted a franchise only weeks before the first draft in 1959, and Wilson still hadn't signed a general manager or coach.
24. (c) Smith leads the way with eleven players; Johnson is second with nine, Jones third with eight, and Williams fourth with six.
25. True. Norwood's percentage of 74.3 percent ranks him sixth all-time.
26. Thurman Thomas.
27. Chuck Dickerson.
28. (d) Bennett, who won the honor in 1987.
29. Norm Pollom, the Bills' former scouting director.
30. The replacement game between the Bills and Giants on October 18, 1987, in which Buffalo won, 6–3, in overtime on a 27-yard field goal by Orchard Park native Todd Schlopy.
31. Ken Stabler in 1976; Bert Jones in 1976; Dan Marino in 1984; and Joe Montana in 1984, '87, and '89.
32. True. Eric Metcalf of the Browns returned a kickoff 90 yards for a touchdown in Cleveland's 34–30 playoff victory against the Bills.
33. (c) John Nies
34. Butch Rolle
35. (b) 214 on just 18 carries.
36. Steve Freeman and Booker Edgerson.
37. Two, a 52-yarder and a 50-yarder early in the '91 season.
38. The University of Washington.
39. True. But the New York Titans drafted him in a secret meeting held by the owners weeks before the official draft. AFL Commissioner Joe Foss heard about the unofficial draft and declared it null and void, much to the anger of Titans' owner Harry Wismer, who thought the league would have a better chance of succeeding by having the most recognizable college player performing in the Big Apple.
40. Simpson (1969), Smith (1985), Cousineau (1979), Patulski (1972).
41. No.
42. Earl Morrall.
43. Bill Walsh.

44. True. The Bills are a perfect 5–0 at Rich in the post-season.
45. (d) Ed Rutkowski averaged 30.50 on 13 returns during the 1963 season.
46. O.J. Simpson (1973 and 1975) and Thurman Thomas (1991).
47. (a) Jeff Wright had six despite missing seven games because of a knee injury.
48. James Lofton.
49. False. Kelly had 15 TDs and 17 interceptions in post-season play.
50. Guard Billy Shaw, defensive tackle Tom Sestak, and safety George Saimes.

ABOUT THE AUTHOR

Scott Pitoniak has covered the Buffalo Bills for the Rochester (New York) *Democrat* and *Chronicle* for the past seven seasons. During that time, the magna cum laude graduate of Syracuse University has won twenty-four national and regional writing awards. His work has appeared in the *Washington Post, USA Today, Chicago Tribune, Sport* magazine, *Inside Sports, The Sporting News,* and numerous other major magazines and newspapers. A native of Rome, New York, Pitoniak resides in Rochester with his wife, Susan, and their children, Amy and Christopher.